A Hand for Spelling

A spelling scheme in joined writing

BOOK 3b

By Charles Cripps

A Hand for Spelling Book 3b
Ref 01626
ISBN 1 85503 211 2

First published 1988
New edition 1995
Reprinted 1997

LDA, Duke Street, Wisbech, Cambs PE13 2AE

Contact our customer services department to find out more about the complete *A Hand For Spelling* range. Tel: 01945 463441 Fax: 01945 587361

The Author

Charles Cripps was formerly a tutor at the University of Cambridge Institute of Education. The focus of his work is on communication skills for children with learning difficulties.

He lectures nationally and internationally on the teaching of spelling and handwriting and has contributed to the National Curriculum proposals. He has many publications including: *The Hand for Spelling Dictionary*, LDA; co-author with Robin Cox of *Joining the ABC*, LDA, as well as a range of *Stile®* and software publications for the teaching of spelling.

This revised edition of *A Hand for Spelling* is the result of ongoing classroom investigation regarding the link between the teaching of joined writing and the catching of spelling.

Charles Cripps would also like to acknowledge the valuable contribution to the revised edition by Janet Ede. Many of the spelling activities are based on, or have been taken directly from, the original Activity Books in which Janet Ede was the co-author.

Charles Cripps is also grateful to Robin Cox for his advice on the content of the programme and to Jo Finch for the idea of letter formation snakes in Book 1a.

Introduction

The National Curriculum has presented schools with a new agenda for the teaching of handwriting. At all Key Stages the importance of well-formed legible handwriting is emphasised. There has also been a gradual acceptance of the value of children beginning joined writing from a much earlier age. It is no longer the sole responsibility of teachers in the junior years. The new proposals now require children to produce handwriting which is joined and legible at Level 3 in Key Stage 1.

The requirements of the National Curriculum are totally endorsed and supported within *A Hand for Spelling*. The rationale behind this programme also argues that the Level Descriptions as outlined in the National Curriculum can best be met when teachers recognise the value of introducing children to joined writing from the beginning. This programme is based on the strong principle that the free physical movement through the word contributes to success in spelling.

Revised Edition

This revised edition is the result of ongoing investigation in the classroom into the teaching of spelling and joined writing. It offers the following features:

▷ Each letter pattern is introduced with a section concentrating on handwriting where letters are produced in a connected form. This is followed by work on the spelling of words with that pattern. Activities providing practice and consolidation follow on directly from each letter pattern.

▷ A new section on p.viii sets out the rationale behind the teaching of joined writing and spelling and gives suggestions on good practice. Pages x-xi give guidelines on how to use the worksheets and how to select worksheets appropriately to meet the needs of an individual pupil.

▷ A complete contents list for the whole scheme enables you to pinpoint letter patterns required to meet the needs of groups or individual pupils.

▷ Finally, because *A Hand for Spelling* is a spelling scheme in joined writing, it leaves you free to adopt any handwriting style, as might have been agreed in the school policy. However, this new edition does provide an improved model which offers a clear, consistent demonstration of movement through letters and the joins between letters.

Contents

A Hand for Spelling has been designed as a spelling scheme in joined writing and provides you with material to cover the teaching of spelling and handwriting as outlined in the National Curriculum.

Books 1a and 1b introduce children to a range of pre-writing activities to promote pencil control and correct letter formation.

A Hand For Spelling Phonetic Stage introduces children, who are at the phonetic stage of spelling, to write words which contain the same letter pattern and the same sound unit. This is an important developmental stage which children reach and requires practice before passing through to the transitional stage and onto standard or correct spelling.

Books 2a to 4b provide children with the opportunity of writing letter patterns and then looking at words containing the same letter pattern irrespective of their sound. All the words used in this programme are a careful selection based on the words used by 5-11 year-old children in their writing.

A Hand for Spelling Book 1a

Book 1a gives children practice in pencil control and fine motor movements. Scribbles and patterns will also help develop pencil control, visual perception and hand-eye co-ordination. It is important that these are practised in art media as well as with the pencil or crayon. The final worksheets in Book 1a help children learn to recognise and write the individual letters. It is at this stage that they must also begin to learn correct letter formation and the names of the letters.

A Hand for Spelling Book 1b

Book 1b supports and helps to cement the skills introduced in Book 1a. Pencil control and correct letter formation are essential prerequisites before moving on to Book 2a or the Phonetic Stage book. When practising the letters the children should continue using the names of the letters.

These books are based on words used by children aged 5-7

Phonetic Stage

The Phonetic Stage provides practice, within the phonetic stage of spelling, of writing words which contain the same spelling pattern and the same sound. Although children are writing down what they <u>hear</u> it is also important to begin promoting the visual aspect of spelling, that is, encourage the children to write down what they <u>see</u>. Therefore, when practising these letter patterns the children should continue to use the letter names. The words in this book contain the five short vowel sounds. With the exception of the 'ch', 'sh', 'th', 'qu' beginnings and the 'ck', 'll', 'ss' endings, all words begin and end with single consonants only.

A Hand For Spelling Books 3a and 3b

These books are based on words used by children aged 7-9.

A Hand for Spelling Books 4a and 4b

These books are based on words used by children aged 9-11.

The Teaching of Handwriting

The National Curriculum emphasises the importance of handwriting by stating that by the end of Key Stage 1, children should have developed a comfortable handwriting style which is joined and legible.

The inference taken from this statement is that children should be introduced as early as possible to the making of letters through patterns. Pre-school children do a great deal of scribbling and inventive writing. They should be encouraged at this stage, and in the reception class, to discover letter shapes and movements in these forms. The shapes and movements should then be developed into making letters in connected form.

The teaching of joined writing from as early as possible has many advantages:

▷ It is no longer necessary to make the change from print to joined writing at Levels 2 and 3.

▷ From the beginning it will be clear to children that words are separate. This helps children to acquire the concept of a 'word' from the very early stages of writing.

▷ Correct letter formation is encouraged from the beginning since the ligatures lead naturally into the correct starting point for each letter.

▷ Joined writing helps children to develop a legible style that exhibits 'regularity of size and shape of letters' (a requirement of Key Stage 1).

▷ Good spelling is encouraged because letter patterns are necessarily connected when writing a word.

COMMON CONCERNS

The following concerns are commonly raised by teachers.

Are children able to read joined writing and will it present any problems in early reading?

The only practical implication is that children should have a chance to read both print and joined writing. The sensible level of discussion with children who are beginning to read will support the need to spot the differences and to talk about letters, joins and whole words. Certainly joined writing should be used when writing in a child's book although both joined writing and print script may be used in displays around the school and classroom. Words which are for reading only are likely to be in print and words that are likely to be written should be in joined writing. In other words there is a style for reading and a style for writing. Experience has shown, however, that children are able to read both.

How should capital letters be taught?

Capital letters are printed and it is not necessary to join them to the lower case letter.

Won't the early teaching of joined writing affect legibility?

In any handwriting programme, the first priority should be legibility. If handwriting is the means of communication then it must be easy to read with letters properly formed. At a later stage, children will require different levels of writing for different purposes, namely a very fast hand for personal notes; a clear but quick hand for general use and finally a formal hand for special occasions. The second priority is speed, because speed of writing has been shown to influence spelling. In most cases the fast printer is not as fast as the writer who uses a cursive style.

Does it matter what handwriting style we use with A Hand for Spelling?

No. *A Hand for Spelling* leaves children free to use any style of handwriting. However, in line with National Curriculum recommendations, children must be encouraged to develop a personal style by breaking away from the taught model. This will only be successful if the foundations are secure. The personal hand usually begins to take shape towards the end of the primary years and is an indication of the writer's confidence and maturity.

TEACHING POINTS

In delivering a handwriting programme, attention should also be given to the following:

▷ Allow plenty of practice of pre-writing skills involving scribbling and pattern work which will help develop perception and hand-eye co-ordination. This can also link in with art and craft work.

▷ Observe how children form their letters at all stages and be careful not to be influenced by the look or appearance of the finished product, if done unobserved.

▷ The teaching of print should not be neglected and can be introduced as art work. At the beginning of Key Stage 2 children should be taught to develop 'legible handwriting in both joined up and printed styles'.

▷ Give specific attention to pencil control, pencil grip and posture, being alert to the different needs of left-handed children. (Assorted pencil grips are available from LDA.)

LEFT-HANDED CHILDREN

Provision must be made for left-handed children. If these children are taught *how to be left-handed* then they can write as freely and legibly as right-handed children. The following practical considerations all help.

▷ Left-handers should always sit on the left-hand side of a right-hander. This will avoid their arms colliding.

▷ The left-hander needs to have the paper on the left hand side of the mid line of the body. After tilting the paper to a comfortable angle it should be pushed about five centimetres away from the body. Incorrect paper position will usually result in an awkward, twisted grip. Some left-handers may need to hold the pencil a little further away from the point than right-handers so that the writing is not obscured by the thumb knuckle.

▷ Ideally, left-handers should have the light coming over the left shoulder.

▷ It is also important for left-handers to sit on a higher chair. This position, together with the paper being pushed away from the body, will prevent the elbow locking into the side of the body when the writing has reached only half way across the page.

▷ In A Hand for Spelling the design of some activities which demand writing from memory are more suitable for right-handed children. The teacher may therefore wish to make a model more suitable for left-handed children by cutting and pasting the appropriate pages before photocopying.

The Teaching of Spelling

It has been shown that good handwriting and spelling go together: the work of Cripps and Cox (1989) indicates that where the two skills are taught together, children do become more confident in looking at and writing words. They are more willing to 'have a go' and are certainly more able to look critically at their work and identify misspellings. It is therefore logical and more economic to link the teaching of spelling to the teaching of handwriting.

In order to promote spelling through handwriting it is important that children practise patterns or strings of letters which belong to the English writing system. This means that if, for example, children are rehearsing 'ood', then they would be encouraged to use this pattern in words such as 'good', 'wood', and 'food'. The most significant difference in this word group compared with the lists of words traditionally used for spelling is that they are grouped according to *visual structure*. This is because it is primarily by *looking* that we remember spelling. If we are uncertain about how to write a word then we write it down to see if it looks right. The decision about correctness can be made when the word is seen written down.

In the early stages of writing development it is true that children do rely on what they hear. They write 'wot' for 'what', because the word sounds like 'pot', 'hot', 'not', etc. They also write 'sed' for 'said' and 'thay' for 'they'. This is the phonetic stage of spelling and it is for this reason that the words in the Phonetic Stage book are grouped according to sound and visual appearance only. However, if children are to become confident spellers we must help them to cultivate visual skills. In other words, they must always be encouraged to look at the whole word and try to write down what they *see* rather than what they *hear*.

You can also promote the catching of spelling by helping children to look for words within words. Children can begin to look for common letter patterns by starting with those that occur in their own names. During any discussion with children about the look of a word you should always use the letter names rather than the sounds, because it is the names that provide the only reliable and consistent way of describing the spelling of a word.

It is important that children learn to write words 'from memory'. This can be done by encouraging children to look closely at a word before writing it. You can point out the interesting features and challenge the child to reproduce the word without copying. It is here that handwriting becomes so important because 'speed of writing is clearly basic to spelling progress' (Peters, 1985) and speed is determined by legibility and letter formation. Where writing from memory is continually encouraged, the qualitative level of spelling is much higher.

Obviously teachers must be careful that children do not become so concerned about the secretarial skills of spelling and handwriting that the essential composing aspects are lost. Spelling and handwriting serve writing and their prime function is to convey legibly the writer's message to the reader.

The teacher who maintains a careful balance between compositional skills on the one hand and the importance of word inspection and writing the different word structures on the other, will find that children's confidence and pleasure in writing will increase.

Using A Hand for Spelling

STRUCTURE OF THE SCHEME

A Hand for Spelling consists of nine books of photocopy masters designed for 5-11 year-olds and older pupils with learning difficulties.

The first stage follows on from the natural, free scribble movements which children make when they first hold a pencil. These are then harnessed into pattern work from which a running hand will follow. Books 1a and 1b develop these pre-writing skills and give children practice in pencil control and fine motor movements before introducing letter formation.

After Book 1b the activities give children the opportunity of looking at and writing words which contain common letter patterns. They teach them to join letters together as early as possible. Lines are not used because they are not necessary for the development of movement and can inhibit the natural flow.

The words used in each book have been selected from the known writing vocabularies of children and are presented in the following age bands:

	Ages	Key Stage	Year Groups
Book 1a, 1b, Phonetic Stage, 2a, 2b	5-7	1	1-2
Books 3a, 3b	7-9	1 & 2	3-4
Books 4a, 4b	9-11	2	5-6

> **Important Note**
> *With the exception of Book 1a and 1b, which are graded, Books a and b are at the same level. For example, Book 2a begins with one and two-letter patterns, moving through to three and four-letter patterns in Book 2b. Together the two books form a complete resource for Key Stage 1. Books 3a and 3b and 4a and 4b are arranged in the same way.*

SELECTING WORKSHEETS

Within each of the books, the worksheets are presented alphabetically, not in order of difficulty. This enables you to select the most appropriate worksheets to meet the needs of the group or individual child. Some worksheets may be needed on more than one occasion.

Some words appear on more than one worksheet. This is either because the letter pattern is repeated across the age ranges with more complex words at a higher level, or because the words contain more than one letter pattern. For example, 'there' appears on the worksheet with 'ere' and the 'the' letter patterns.

The examples below illustrate how worksheets may be selected according to the needs of the group or individual child.

Sam Sed it was his.

↓

This misspelling of 'said' reflects the phonetic stage, that is, there is a match between letter and sound, and 'the alternative is phonetically plausible' (Level Description 2).

↓

The most appropriate approach in this situation is for a child to practise the letter pattern 'sai'. In practising this letter pattern, the movement of the hand through the letters will help the child to 'feel' and then look at other words with a similar structure at the beginning. In this instance, linking 'said' with 'sail' will also help with the visual aspect and discourage reliance on sound.

↓

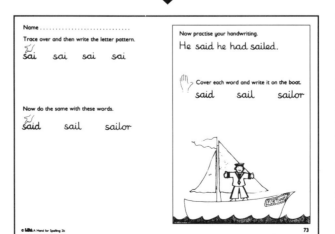

Mum Siad it was good.

↓

This misspelling of 'said' reflects the transitional stage, that is, there is evidence of some visual awareness of the letters required for the word 'said'.

↓

The most appropriate approach is to promote the fact that visually 'said' is an 'aid' word. This means relating it to other 'aid' words, for example, 'maid, paid, raid' etc. Although these words also contain the same sound they must be described as 'a-i-d' words. This is a spelling activity, not 'phonetics for reading'. Once again the movement through the word will also help with the visual aspects of the word 'said'.

↓

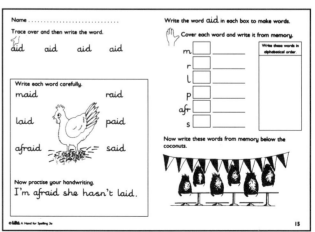

USING THE WORKSHEETS

Each worksheet is designed to give children the opportunity of practising a particular letter pattern in joined writing before moving on to work which focuses on spelling.

On each worksheet there is a mixture of print and joined writing. Instructions, which are for reading, are in print whilst the joined writing, which can also be read, provides the model for handwriting.

Before beginning the worksheet, check the child can read the words. Some children may require help with word recognition and as a result may resort to a phonic approach, that is, decoding. For reading this is perfectly acceptable because 'sounding out' is an important word attack skill. When the child has read (decoded) the word and is asked how to write it the response should be by the names of the letters.

Discuss the formation of the letter pattern. Always use the names of the letters.

This activity helps to cement the letter pattern and the spelling of these words.

Ensure each letter is formed correctly. This may mean continual observation.

Although the sounds are different always describe the pattern as a 'a-n-t' word.

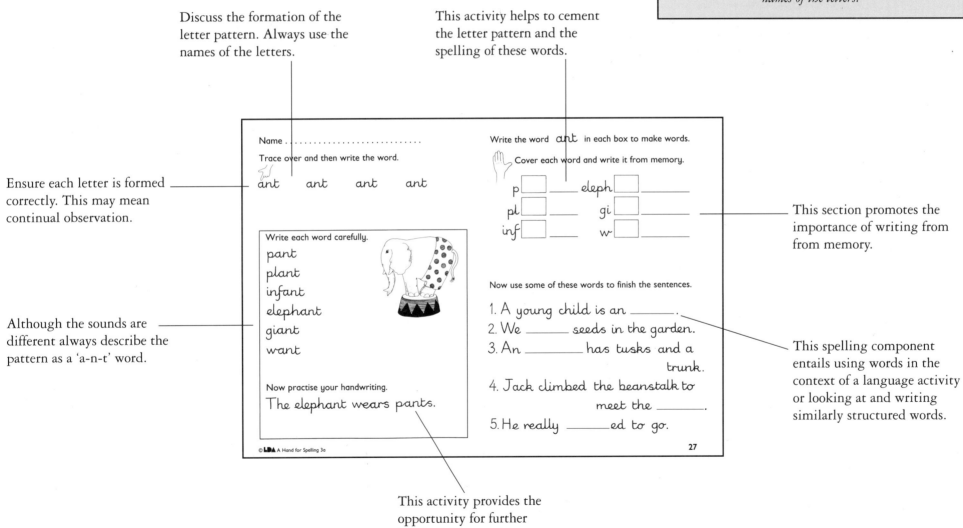

Name . . . .

Trace over and then write the word.

ant   ant   ant   ant

Write each word carefully.

pant
plant
infant
elephant
giant
want

Now practise your handwriting.

The elephant wears pants.

© LDA A Hand for Spelling 3a

Write the word *ant* in each box to make words.

Cover each word and write it from memory.

p ☐ _____   eleph ☐ _____
pl ☐ _____   gi ☐ _____
inf ☐ _____   w ☐ _____

Now use some of these words to finish the sentences.

1. A young child is an _____ .
2. We _____ seeds in the garden.
3. An _____ has tusks and a trunk.
4. Jack climbed the beanstalk to meet the _____ .
5. He really _____ed to go.

27

This section promotes the importance of writing from from memory.

This spelling component entails using words in the context of a language activity or looking at and writing similarly structured words.

This activity provides the opportunity for further handwriting practice.

LETTER FORMATION

Some capital letters are used, for example, the personal pronoun 'I' and the letter 'C' as in 'Christmas'. The style recommended for all capital letters is bold print with no join to the lower case letter.

The letters 'g', 'j' and 'y' do not join fully because a fully looped letter can be difficult for young children. This style also encourages the use of some pen lifts which will be essential for writing with speed later on.

What is important is the movement through the word, so for words containing these letters the procedure is as follows.

▷ If the word begins with a 'g', 'j', or 'y' then it is formed as a single letter, with the following letter beginning from the position it was taught as a single flowing letter.

▷ If the letters 'g', 'j', or 'y' appear within the word then they are joined to the preceding letter in the usual way, but completed as a single letter. The following letter begins from the position it was taught as a single letter.

The apostrophe is used in contractions such as 'didn't' and 'hasn't', hence the reason for its usage will need to be taught.

Check Points

SPELLING

✓ Collect and talk about words containing common letter patterns.

✓ Look for words within words. Visual discrimination of word form is a crucial part of learning how words are structured.

✓ Encourage the 'Look-Cover-Write-Check' routine. Remember that the important aspect of this routine is the writing from memory.

✓ Never ask a child whether a spelling is 'right'. This only promotes the unhelpful notion of 'right and wrong' and is damaging to self image if the word is 'wrong'. Instead, encourage visual inspection of the word by asking, 'Is yours the same as this?' If not, then ask, 'What do you need to do to make it the same?'

✓ Encourage children to verbalise their attempts at difficult words.

✓ Provide opportunities for children to write words in context as well as writing letter patterns.

HANDWRITING

✓ Provide pre-writing activities to promote pencil control.

✓ Teach a pencil grip which is firm but relaxed. The pencil should be held between the thumb and first finger, resting against the middle finger.

✓ Ensure correct posture with children sitting comfortably, with feet flat on the floor and body upright, but tilted slightly forward on a chair suited to the height of the table.

✓ Children should have good light in order to see what they are writing without straining the eye. The writing position should be comfortable and the paper correctly angled to suit either left or right-handers.

✓ Ensure correct letter formation at all times. See pages xiii and xiv for letter formation for both left and right-handed children.

✓ Always encourage movement through the letter pattern or word.

✓ Teach and use letter pattern names and not sounds.

✓ Develop a language of writing which will enable the children to understand and verbalise the physical actions required when writing.

✓ Teach the meanings of words such as: top, bottom, up, down, round, over, back, letter, word, pattern, left, right, join, curved, straight, ascenders, descenders, etc.

✓ Encourage children to discuss the quality of their own handwriting, looking at the letter formation etc.

✓ Encourage children to use different standards of writing for different purposes.

✓ Ensure that children acquire legibility in both print and cursive styles.

✓ Give careful attention to the different needs of left-handed children.

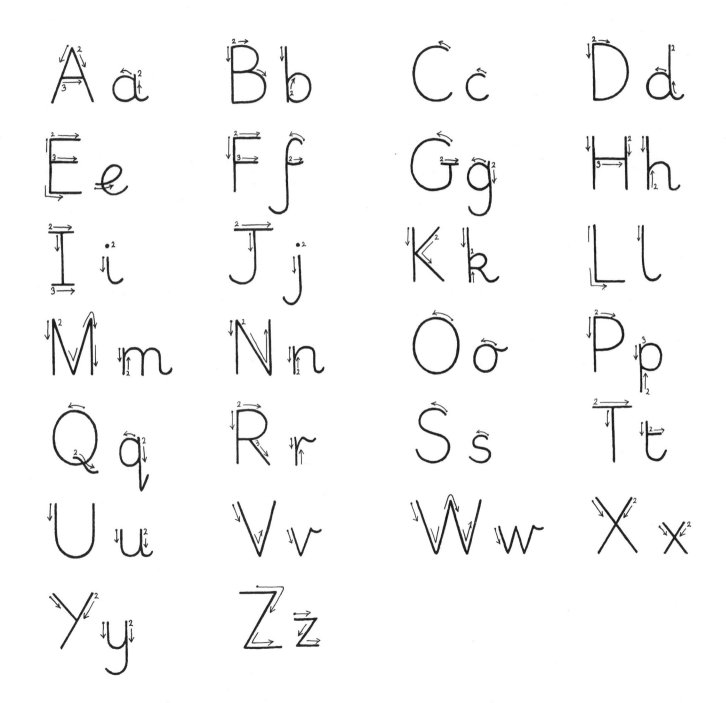

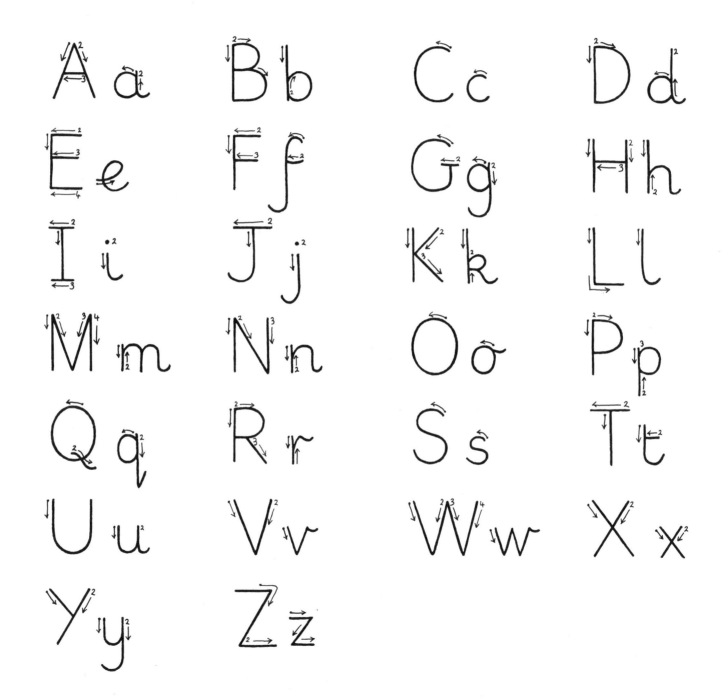

Name . . . .

Trace over and then write the letter pattern.

oes   oes   oes   oes

Write each word carefully.

does

doesn't

goes

toes

potatoes

shoes

Now practise your handwriting.

He does like potatoes.

Write the letter pattern oes in each box to make words.

Cover each word and write it from memory.

d ☐ _____   t ☐ _____

d ☐ n't _____   potat ☐ _____

g ☐ _____   sh ☐ _____

Use some of these words to finish the poem.

My friend Joel
Has _____ with holes.
But what really shocks
Is, he _____ wear socks.
So, wherever he _____,
You can see all his _____!

Name . . . .

Trace over and then write the letter pattern.

oke oke oke oke

Write each word carefully.

woke   awoke

spoke   smoke

broke

Now practise your handwriting.

She spoke when she woke.

Write the letter pattern **oke** in each box to make words.

Cover each word and write it from memory.

w ☐ _____

aw ☐ _____

sp ☐ _____

sm ☐ _____

br ☐ _____

Now finish the story using some of these words. Remember to use capital letters and full stops.

On bonfire night we had a blazing fire . . . .

_____

_____

_____

_____

2

Name . . . .

Trace over and then write the word.

old   old   old   old

Write each word carefully.

cold
told
fold
sold
hold
soldier

Now practise your handwriting.

The soldier was cold.

Write the word old in each box to make words.

Cover each word and write it from memory.

c ☐ ____   s ☐ ____

t ☐ ____   h ☐ ____

f ☐ ____   s ☐ ier ____

Now sort out these jumbled sentences.

1. were told bike We sold. was that

_____

2. hold book me. Please this for

_____

Name . . . .

Trace over and then write the letter pattern.

ome   ome   ome   ome

Write each word carefully.

home   come

some   women

Now practise your handwriting.

Come home soon.

Write the letter pattern ome in each box to make words.

Cover each word and write it from memory.

h⬚ _____

c⬚ _____

s⬚ _____

w⬚n _____

Now use these words to fill in the opposites.

_____ or away

_____ or none

men and _____

_____ or go

4

Name . . . .

Trace over and then write the word.

one   one   one   one

Write each word carefully.

gone

bone

telephone

money

honey

Now practise your handwriting.

His honey has gone.

Write the word one in each box to make words.

Cover each word and write it from memory.

n ☐ _____   m ☐ y _____

g ☐ _____   h ☐ y _____

b ☐ _____

teleph ☐ _____

Now use some of these words to finish the poem.

It's really very funny
I haven't any _____.
I thought I had a pound
But when I looked I found
My pound had really _____.
Disappeared! I had _____.

Name . . . .

Trace over and then write the letter pattern.

ood   ood   ood   ood

Write each word carefully.

good

wood

stood

food

flood

blood

Now practise your handwriting.

The food is good!

Write the letter pattern ood in each box to make words.

Cover each word and write it from memory.

g ☐ _____   w ☐ _____

st ☐ _____   f ☐ _____

fl ☐ _____   bl ☐ _____

Use some ood words to finish the poem.

Deep in the _____

An oak tree _____.

It had lived since the days

of Robin _____.

It had seen battles

And storms and _____.

The oak tree had secrets

Written in _____!

Name . . . .

Trace over and then write the letter pattern.

ook   ook   ook   ook

Write each word carefully.

cookery

hook

took

look

book

shook

Now practise your handwriting.

He took a look at the cookery book.

Write the letter pattern ook in each box to make words.

Cover each word and write it from memory.

c ▢ ____   h ▢ ____

t ▢ ____   l ▢ ____

b ▢ ____   sh ▢ ____

Now finish the patterns.

shake	shaken	
		took

cook			
	hooks		
		looking	
			booked

Name . . . .

Trace over and then write the letter pattern.

ool   *ool*   *ool*   *ool*

Write each word carefully.

cool

pool

stool

tools

school

wool

Now practise your handwriting.

The pool was cool.

Write the letter pattern *ool* in each box to make words.

Cover each word and write it from memory.

c [ ] _____

p [ ] _____

st [ ] _____

t [ ] s _____

sch [ ] _____

w [ ] _____

Write these words in alphabetical order.

How many *ool* words can you find in the word search?

h	y	p	e	c	o	o	l	i
f	l	k	s	c	h	o	o	l
e	p	o	o	l	s	e	d	y
r	e	t	o	o	l	s	e	t
o	v	w	o	o	l	l	e	n
f	o	o	l	b	r	o	o	s
e	m	n	d	s	t	o	o	l
e	w	o	o	l	e	r	s	o
o	o	f	o	o	l	i	s	h

Name . . . .

Trace over and then write the letter pattern.

oom oom oom oom

Write each word carefully.

room

bedroom

bloom

gloomy

Now practise your handwriting.

The blooms cheered the room.

Write the letter pattern oom in each box to make words.

 Cover each word and write it from memory.

r ☐ _____

bedr ☐ _____

bl ☐ _____

gl ☐ y _____

Now use the apostrophe.

the room
of

Gran's room

_____

the car
of

Mum's car

_____

the room
of

David's bedroom

_____

the cake
of

Maria's cake

_____

Name . . . .

Trace over and then write the letter pattern.

oon   oon   oon   oon

Write each word carefully.

soon   moon

noon   spoon

Now practise your handwriting.

It will soon be noon.

Write the letter pattern oon in each box to make words.

Cover each word and write it from memory.

s ☐ _____   n ☐ _____

m ☐ _____   sp ☐ _____

Now use these words to finish the sentences.

1. There will be a full _____ tonight.
2. And the dish ran away with the _____.
3. Dad will be back very _____.
4. She had her lunch at _____.

10

Trace over and then write the letter pattern.

oot   oot   oot   oot

Write each word carefully.

root   boot

shoot

foot

Now practise your handwriting.

I wore a boot on my foot.

Write the letter pattern oot in each box to make words.

Cover each word and write it from memory.

r ☐ ___   sh ☐ ___

b ☐ ___   f ☐ ___

Now read through this story and correct the spelling mistakes.

All year I'd wonted to play in the scool futball team but either somone else was chosen or I was away. Then at last my chance came. With my new bootes I was sure I woud be able to shute for the winning goal – and hear, "Emma your'e the champ!"

Name . . . .

Trace over and then write the letter pattern.

orn   orn   orn   orn

Write each word carefully.

horn

born

corn

corner

worn

morning

Now practise your handwriting.

She was born in the morning.

Write the letter pattern orn in each box to make words.

Cover each word and write it from memory.

h ☐ _____   c ☐ er _____

b ☐ _____   w ☐ _____

c ☐ _____   m ☐ ing _____

Now use some of these words to finish the puzzle.

The early part of the day. ☐

Used to sound a warning from a car. ☐

Breakfast flakes are made of this. ☐

Four on a square, three on a triangle. ☐

Your birthday celebrates the day you were... ☐

Name . . . .

Trace over and then write the letter pattern.

ost   ost   ost   ost

Write each word carefully.

cost

frost

post

most

almost

ghost

Now practise your handwriting.

Frost almost froze the ghost.

Write the letter pattern ost in each box to make words.

Cover each word and write it from memory.

c ☐ ____   m ☐ ____

fr ☐ ____   alm ☐ ____

p ☐ ____   gh ☐ ____

Use ost words to finish the weather forecast.

In _____ parts of the country the temperature will drop to _____ freezing. Indeed, some places will have a touch of _____. In the morning there will be thick fog in all parts, so if you're out early, don't get _____.

Name . . . .

Trace over and then write the letter pattern.

oth   oth   oth   oth

Write each word carefully.

cloth

bother

both

clothes

clothing

Now practise your handwriting.

The moth ate the clothes.

Write the letter pattern oth in each box to make words.

Cover each word and write it from memory.

cl[   ] _____

b[   ]er _____

b[   ] _____

cl[   ]es _____

cl[   ]ing _____

Find the oth words with similar meanings.

Annoy   [   ]

Material   [   ]

Garments   [   ]

The two
of them   [   ]

Name . . . .

Trace over and then write the letter pattern.

ott   ott   ott   ott

Write each word carefully.

bottom   cotton

bottle   throttle

cottage

Now practise your handwriting.

a pretty cottage

Write the letter pattern ott in each box to make words.

Cover each word and write it from memory.

b ☐ om _____

c ☐ on _____

b ☐ le _____

thr ☐ le _____

c ☐ age _____

Now use some of these words to fill the boxes.

the lowest part   ☐

a small house   ☐

thread for sewing   ☐

part of an engine   ☐

Name . . . .

Trace over and then write the letter pattern.

oud oud oud oud

Write each word carefully.

loud   aloud

cloud   proud

Now practise your handwriting.

The proud man was loud.

Write the letter pattern oud in each box to make words.

Cover each word and write it from memory.

l ☐ _____   al ☐ _____

d ☐ _____   pr ☐ _____

Now finish the pattern.

	louder	
proud		proudest

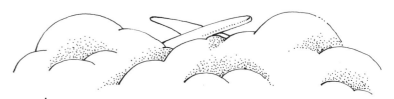

Use oud words to fill in the opposites.

_____ or quiet

humble or _____

clear or _____ y

Name . . . .

Trace over and then write the word.

our our our our

Write each word carefully.

hour flour pour

colour honour neighbour

favourite journey

Now practise your handwriting.

Our journey will take an hour.

Write the word **Our** in each box to make words.

Cover each word and write it from memory.

h ☐ _____ fav ☐ ite _____

fl ☐ _____ j ☐ ney _____

p ☐ _____

col ☐ _____

hon ☐ _____

neighb ☐ _____

Now finish the pattern.

hour	
	colours
	neighbours
favourite	

Name . . . .

Trace over and then write the word.

out   out   out   out

Write each word carefully.

about   shout

trout   route

Now practise your handwriting.
We shout out on the route.

Write the word out in each box to make words.

Cover each word and write it from memory.

ab☐   _____

sh☐   _____

tr☐   _____

r☐e   _____

Now use out words to finish the poem.

When we're _____ and _____
We sing and we _____ .
We make such a din and a fuss
We can't read the map
Or follow the _____ ,
So we get out and hop on a bus.

Name . . . .

Trace over and then write the letter pattern.

ove   *ove*   *ove*   *ove*

Write the letter pattern **ove** in each box to make words.

Cover each word and write it from memory.

m [ ] _____   pr [ ] _____

dr [ ] _____   st [ ] _____

ab [ ] _____   gl [ ] _____

Now finish the pattern.

move		
	proved	
		loving
shove		

Write each word carefully.

move   prove

drove   stove

above   glove

Now practise your handwriting.

The bread is above the stove.

Now use **ove** words to find the opposites.

_____ or below

_____ or hate

under or _____

Name . . . .

Trace over and then write the word.

own   own   own   own

Write each word carefully.

town   down

clown   known

Now practise your handwriting.

The clown fell down.

Write the word OWN in each box to make words.

Cover each word and write it from memory.

t [   ] _____

d [   ] _____

cl [   ] _____

kn [   ] _____

Now read through this story and correct the spelling mistakes.

If he had knowen the buket was full of water the clown would have run away. But he got soaked. He sliped and slithered accross the ring, until finally he fell doun.

Name . . . .

Trace over and then write the word.

par   par   par   par

Write each word carefully.

parade

paragraph

separate

parents

parcel

parties

Now practise your handwriting.

Pass the parcel at the party.

Write the word par in each box to make words.

Cover each word and write it from memory.

☐ ade   _____

☐ agraph   _____

se ☐ ate   _____

☐ ents   _____

☐ cel   _____

☐ ties   _____

Now write these words from memory on the parachutes.

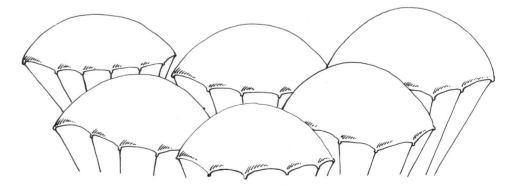

The same as package is _____.

Name . . . .

Trace over and then write the word.

pen   pen   pen   pen

Write each word carefully.

spend   spent

open

pencil

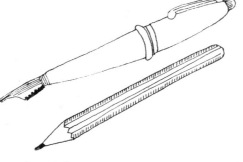

Now practise your handwriting.

a pen and pencil set

Write the word pen in each box to make words.

Cover each word and write it from memory.

s [   ] d _____

s [   ] t _____

o [   ]   _____

[   ] cil _____

Now use these words to spend your holiday money.

I had £5 for my birthday.
I _____ £2 on a pen and _____
set.
I will _____ £1 on a puzzle
book.
How much money will I have
left to _____ a bank account? [   ]

22

Name . . . .

Trace over and then write the letter pattern.

per   *per*   *per*   *per*

Write each word carefully.

perhaps   person

perfume   period

Now practise your handwriting.

That person is wearing perfume.

Write the letter pattern *per* in each box to make words.

Cover each word and write it from memory.

☐ haps _____

☐ son _____

☐ fume _____

☐ iod _____

Now use these words to finish the dictionary list.

_____ a pleasant smell

_____ possibly

_____ a length of time

_____ man, woman or child

Name . . . .

Trace over and then write the letter pattern.

pro   pro   pro   pro

Write each word carefully.

promise

probably

programme

Now practise your handwriting.

I've probably missed the programme.

Write the letter pattern pro in each box to make words.

Cover each word and write it from memory.

☐ mise   _____

☐ bably   _____

☐ gramme _____

Now sort out these jumbled sentences.

1. probably swimming I go lunch. after will

_____

2. friend. gave promise my I my to

_____

My favourite TV _____ is

_____

Name . . . .

Trace over and then write the word.

raw   raw   raw   raw

Write each word carefully.

straw

draw

drawer

Now practise your handwriting.

The straws are in the drawer.

Write the word raw in each box to make words.

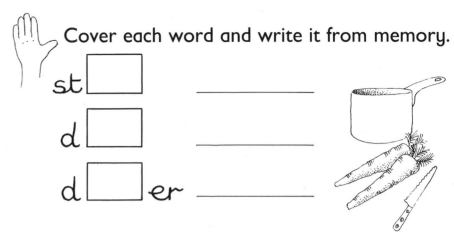

Cover each word and write it from memory.

st ☐ _____

d ☐ _____

d ☐ er _____

Now write a sentence about each picture.

_____

_____

_____

Name . . . .

Trace over and then write the letter pattern.

ree   ree   ree   ree

Write each word carefully.

tree

three

referee

Now practise your handwriting.

Three trees are in the street.

Write the letter pattern ree in each box to make words.

Cover each word and write it from memory.

t [ ] _____

th [ ] _____

refe [ ] _____

Now answer the questions.

Is this eret losing its leaves? ____

Does the football fereere have a whistle? _____

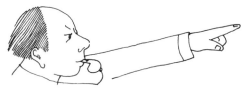

Does four come before reeht ? _____

26

Name . . . .

Trace over and then write the letter pattern.

rew   rew   rew   rew

Write each word carefully.

drew   grew

threw

Now practise your handwriting.

I threw the seeds and they
grew.

Write the letter pattern rew in each box to make
words.

Cover each word and write it from memory.

d ☐ _____

g ☐ _____

th ☐ _____

Now finish the pattern.

grew	grow	
drew		drawn
threw		

The opposite of caught is _____

Trace over and then write the word.

row   row   row   row

Write each word carefully.

grow   throw

arrow   narrow

Now practise your handwriting.

Row the narrow boat.

Write the word **row** in each box to make words.

Cover each word and write it from memory.

g ☐ _____

th ☐ _____

ar ☐ _____

nar ☐ _____

Now read through the story and correct the spelling mistakes.

From inside the castel they saw the army throgh the trees. They had a a pile of stones redy to throe and arows to fire through the narow windows. When the people inside saw so meny soldiers they were afrade. some escaped in a boat which they rowd across the moat.

Name . . . .

Trace over and then write the word.

see   see   see   see

Write each word carefully.

seed   seem

seek   see - saw

Now practise your handwriting.

I can see a see-saw.

Write the word see in each box to make words.

Cover each word and write it from memory.

□d____   □m ____

□k____   □-saw____

Use see words to finish the poem.

I've planted a _____ in this pot,
To _____ if it will grow or not.
I've watered it and kept it warm,
But nothing's to be _____ at all.
It _____s so slow, it should
have grown,
It was this morning it was sown!

Name . . . .

Trace over and then write the word.

the   the   the   the

Write each word carefully.

them   then

these   there

their   they

Now practise your handwriting.

Well then, they've lost them.

Write the word **the** in each box to make words.

Cover each word and write it from memory.

☐ m _____   ☐ n _____

☐ se _____   ☐ re _____

☐ ir _____   ☐ y _____

Now use the letters in the tree to make words starting with **the** .

re
se   m

ir

'n   y

☐   ☐

☐   ☐

☐   ☐

Use **their** and **there** to complete the sentence.

_____ books are over _____ .

© LDA A Hand for Spelling 3b

Name . . . .

Trace over and then write the letter pattern.

tor   tor   tor   tor

Write each word carefully.

torn

story

history

doctor

tractor

visitor

Now practise your handwriting.

The visitor read us a story.

Write the letter pattern tor in each box to make words.

Cover each word and write it from memory.

☐ n _____   doc ☐ _____

s ☐ y _____   trac ☐ _____

his ☐ y _____   visi ☐ _____

Now use some of these words to finish the story.

The _____ told us her _____ about the past. She knew a lot about the _____ of our village. When she was small, most people worked on the land. They used horses to do the work. Now they use _____s instead.

Trace over and then write the letter pattern.

tru   tru   tru   tru

Write each word carefully.

trunk

truck

trust

true

truth

truly

Now practise your handwriting.

The truck took the trunk.

Write the letter pattern   tru   in each box to make words.

Cover each word and write it from memory.

	nk	_____
	ck	_____
	st	_____
	e	_____
	th	_____
	ly	_____

Now use some of these words to finish the poem.

I'm telling the _____,

It's really _____.

You know I would not lie to you.

_____ I tell you

_____ me, please —

Christmas puddings grow on trees!

© LDA A Hand for Spelling 3b

Name . . . .

Trace over and then write the letter pattern.

uck   uck   uck

Write each word carefully.

luck

duck

bucket

Now practise your handwriting.
The duck has a bucket.

Write the letter pattern uck in each box to make words.

Cover each word and write it from memory.

l ☐ ____   b ☐ et ____

d ☐ ____

Now use uck words to finish the story.

In the wood lived an old man, his wife and their pet _____. The old man was un_____y. His hens didn't lay and his corn didn't grow. Then one day his _____ came into the house carrying a _____ in its bill. And what do you think was in the bucket but _____

_____?

Name . . . .

Trace over and then write the letter pattern.

udd   udd   udd   udd

Write each word carefully.

muddy

sudden

muddle

puddle

pudding

Now practise your handwriting.

Splash through a muddy
puddle.

Write the letter pattern udd in each box to make
words.

Cover each word and write it from memory.

m [   ] y   _____

s [   ] en   _____

m [   ] le   _____

p [   ] le   _____

p [   ] ing _____

Now use these words to find similar meanings.

quick _____

small pool of water _____

dessert _____

a mess _____

dirty _____

Name . . . .

Trace over and then write the letter pattern.

uit   uit   uit   uit

Write each word carefully.

biscuit

fruit

quite

Now practise your handwriting.

I quite like fruit and biscuits.

Write the letter pattern uit in each box to make words.

Cover each word and write it from memory.

bisc ☐ _____

fr ☐ _____

q ☐ e _____

My favourite _____s are

_____

My favourite _____ is

_____

I also _____ like

_____

Name . . . .

Trace over and then write the letter pattern.

ull   ull   ull   ull

Write each word carefully.

bull

full

pull

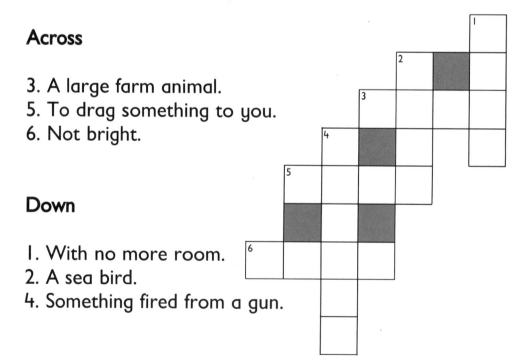

Now practise your handwriting.

The bull pulled.

Write the letter pattern ull in each box to make words.

Cover each word and write it from memory.

b [ ] _____

f [ ] _____

p [ ] _____

Now use ull words to finish the crossword.

Across

3. A large farm animal.
5. To drag something to you.
6. Not bright.

Down

1. With no more room.
2. A sea bird.
4. Something fired from a gun.

Name . . . .

Trace over and then write the letter pattern.

umb   umb   umb   umb

Write each word carefully.

dumb

thumb

number

Now practise your handwriting.

My thumb is numb.

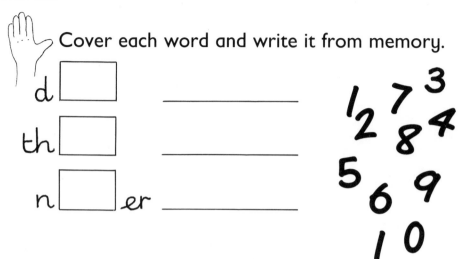

Write the letter pattern umb in each box to make words.

Cover each word and write it from memory.

d ☐ _____

th ☐ _____

n ☐ er _____

1 2 7 3 8 4 5 6 9 1 0

The shaded letters are called vowels.
The others are called consonants.

a b c d e f g h i j k l m n o p q r s t u v w x y z

Now find the vowels to finish the words.

6 1 8 7 5 1 4 9 0 8 9 3

n_mb_rs ☐

th_mb ☐

cr_mb ☐

d_mb ☐

Name . . . .

Trace over and then write the letter pattern.

ump   ump   ump   ump

Write each word carefully.

jump

pump

bump

Now practise your handwriting.

I bump when I jump.

Write the letter pattern **ump** in each box to make words.

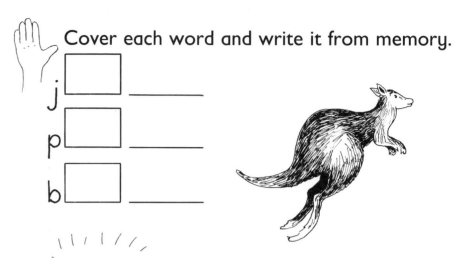

Cover each word and write it from memory.

j ☐ _____

p ☐ _____

b ☐ _____

Now **burst** the words to finish the puzzle.

jumping

jumps — jump — jumped

jumper

bump   dump

Name . . . .

Trace over and then write the letter pattern.

ung   *ung*   *ung*   *ung*

Write the letter pattern **ung** in each box to make words.

Cover each word and write it from memory.

s [ ] ____   h [ ] ry ____

h [ ] ____ :

Now sort out these jumbled sentences.

1. the Which at songs sung were concert? _____

_____

2. was in The picture hall. school hung new the _____

_____

3. swimming children very After hungry. were the _____

_____

Write each word carefully.

sung

hung

hungry

Now practise your handwriting.

Songs were sung and bells rung.

Name . . . .

Trace over and then write the letter pattern.

unn   unn   unn   unn

Write each word carefully.

sunny   funny

tunnel   funnel

Now practise your handwriting.

It was sunny when we came
out of the tunnel.

Write the letter pattern unn in each box to make words.

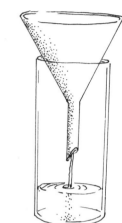

Cover each word and write it from memory.

s [ ] y _____

f [ ] y _____

t [ ] el _____

f [ ] el _____

Now use the code to finish the messages.

| a = ● | e = ▲ | i = ■ | o = ▼ | u = ◆ |

▼n▲ s◆nny d●y my fr■▲nd ●nd

■ pl●y▲d ■n th▲ t◆nn▲l ●t

th▲ f◆nf●◆r

W▲ cr●wl▲d thr▼◆gh ●nd b◆mp▲d

■nt▼ ▲●ch ▼th▲r

■t w●s v▲ry f◆nny.

Name . . . .

Trace over and then write the letter pattern.

ure ure ure

Write each word carefully.

sure   measure

treasure   pleasure

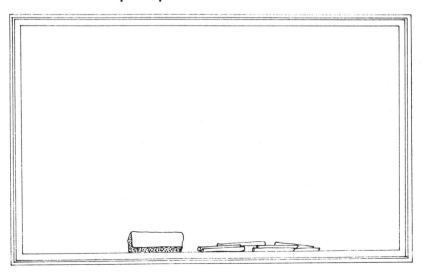

Now practise your handwriting.

Be sure to measure carefully.

Write the letter pattern ure in each box to make words.

Cover each word and write it from memory.

s◻ _____

meas◻ _____

treas◻ _____

pleas◻ _____

Write these words in alphabetical order.

Now find all the ure words.

curemeasurepurepleasuretreasureleisuresure

Name . . . .

Trace over and then write the word.

urn   urn   urn   urn

Write the word urn in each box to make words.

Cover each word and write it from memory.

t [ ] _____

b [ ] _____

ret [ ] _____

Write each word carefully.

turn

burn

return

Now practise your handwriting.

I shall return!

Now read through this story and correct the spelling mistakes.

We made our bonfire from old ferniture, boxes and peices of wood. We took it in turns to throw the rubbish on. It bernt fiercely. Flames crakled and roared. We had to turn away from the heet. The onely thing not to burrn was the old cooker.

Name . . . .

Trace over and then write the word.

use use use use

Write the word use in each box to make words.

Cover each word and write it from memory.

exc [ ] ful _____

exc [ ] _____

m [ ] um _____

ca [ ] _____

beca [ ] _____

Write these words in alphabetical order.

Write each word carefully.

useful

excuse

museum

cause

because

Now practise your handwriting.

I used an excuse not to go.

Use some use words to write in the diary.

DIARY

Sat. 16 Nov.

Name . . . .

Trace over and then write the letter pattern.

ush _ush_ _ush_ _ush_

Write each word carefully.

brush

crush

thrush

bush

push

rush

Now practise your handwriting.

The thrush sang in the bush.

Write the letter pattern _ush_ in each box to make words.

Cover each word and write it from memory.

br ☐ _____   b ☐ _____

cr ☐ _____   p ☐ _____

thr ☐ _____   r ☐ _____

Now _burst_ the words to finish the puzzle.

brushes   brushing

brush

brushed

push   crush

Name . . . .

Trace over and then write the word.

war   war   war   war

Write each word carefully.

ward

reward

warm

warship

Now practise your handwriting.

He was rewarded.

Write the word war in each box to make words.

Cover each word and write it from memory.

☐d _____

re☐d _____

☐m _____

☐ship _____

Across

1. Boat used for battle.
3. Sometimes given for finding a lost pet.
4. Tells of danger.

Down

1. A room in a hospital.
2. Lots of bees.

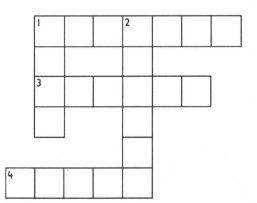

Name . . . .

Trace over and then write the word.

win   win   win   win

Write each word carefully.

wind

windy

window

twins

wing

swing

Now practise your handwriting.

The wind made the window
swing.

Write the word   win   in each box to make words.

Cover each word and write it from memory.

☐ d   ___ t   ☐ s   ___

☐ dy   ___   ☐ g   ___

☐ dow   ___ s   ☐ g   ___

Use win words to finish the poem.

Winter Weather

The _____ blew,

Leaves flew,

Gates were _____ing,

No birds singing.

_____ weather on its way,

Wet and _____ autumn day.

© LDA A Hand for Spelling 3b

Name . . . .

Trace over and then write the letter pattern.

wor   wor   wor   wor

Write the letter pattern **wor** in each box to make words.

Cover each word and write it from memory.

[ ] k _____   [ ] ld _____

[ ] d _____   [ ] n _____

[ ] m _____   s [ ] d _____

Write each word carefully.

work   word   worm

world   worn   sword

Now practise your handwriting.

A worm is at work.

Now use some of these words to finish the story.

A brave knight rode around the _____ in search of a dragon. He was _____ out with searching as it was very hard _____. He couldn't find a dragon but he did see a _____ wriggling out of its hole. He drew his _____ but the _____ smiled and waved – so he couldn't kill it!

Name . . . .

Trace over and then write the word.

you   you   you   you

Write each word carefully.

you'll

you're

your

yourself

young

Now practise your handwriting.

You're only young once.

Write the word you in each box to make words.

Cover each word and write it from memory.

	'll	_____
	're	_____
	r	_____
	rself	_____
	ng	_____

Finish the puzzle.

you are	
	they're
	you'll
she will	

Name . . . .

Trace over and then write the letter pattern.

ance   ance   ance   ance

Write each word carefully.

dance   chance

balance

distance

entrance

Now practise your handwriting.

He lost his balance dancing.

Write the letter pattern ance in each box to make words.

Cover each word and write it from memory.

d [ ] ____   dist [ ] ____

ch [ ] ____   entr [ ] ____

bal [ ] ____

Now finish the pattern.

dance		
	balances	
		glancing
advance		

Now answer the questions.

The opposite of retreat is _____.

The opposite of exit is _____.

Name . . . .

Trace over and then write the letter pattern.

ange   ange   ange   ange

Write each word carefully.

change

strange

danger

orange

Now practise your handwriting.

They've changed to orange.

Write the letter pattern **ange** in each box to make words.

 Cover each word and write it from memory.

ch ☐ _____   str ☐ _____

d ☐ r _____   or ☐ _____

Now use some of these words to finish the crossing code.

Never go on the red light, it's

_____ ous.

After red it's amber, which is

_____ .

Then, when the lights _____ to

green, you can go.

Name . . . .

Trace over and then write the letter pattern.

 atch   atch   atch   atch

Write each word carefully.

catch

match

watch

Now practise your handwriting.

Watch the ball and catch it.

Write the letter pattern atch in each box to make words.

Cover each word and write it from memory.

c ☐ _____

m ☐ _____

w ☐ _____

Now burst the words to finish the puzzle.

matched
↑
matches ← match → matching

↑
← patch →

↑
← watch →

↑
← snatch →

Name . . . .

Trace over and then write the letter pattern.

augh augh augh augh

Write each word carefully.

laugh

laughter

caught

taught

daughter

naughty

Now practise your handwriting.

The naughty daughter laughed.

Write the letter pattern augh in each box to make words.

Cover each word and write it from memory.

l ☐ _____

l ☐ ter _____

c ☐ t _____

t ☐ t _____

d ☐ ter _____

n ☐ ty _____

Now use augh words to finish the poem.

_____ is catching

So they say.

I _____ some only yesterday.

Now, today, I'm _____ing still.

I've _____ so much, I feel

quite ill!

Name . . . .

Trace over and then write the word.

ball   *ball*   *ball*   *ball*

Write each word carefully.

balloon

football

snowball

Now practise your handwriting.

He played snowball football.

Write the word **ball** in each box to make words.

Cover each word and write it from memory.

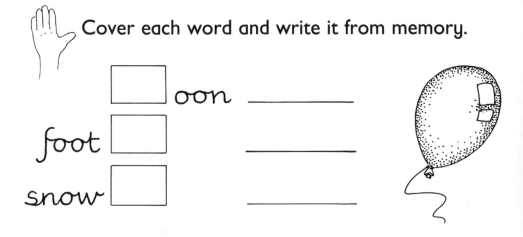

☐oon _____

foot☐ _____

snow☐ _____

Trace over the lines and write the right word in each box.

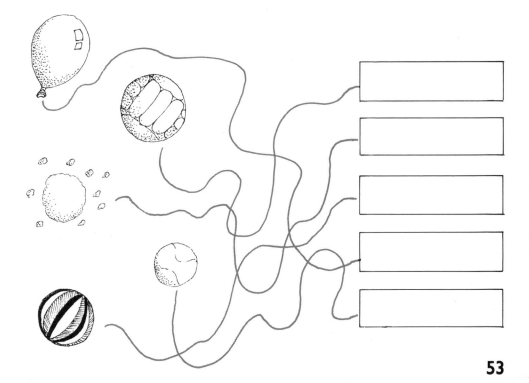

Name . . . .

Trace over and then write the word.

body   body   body   body

Write each word carefully.

anybody   nobody

somebody   everybody

Now practise your handwriting.

Anybody can bodybuild.

Write the word body in each box to make words.

Cover each word and write it from memory.

any ☐ _____

no ☐ _____

some ☐ _____

every ☐ _____

Now help the body builder to find the body words.

some   every

body

any   no

_____   _____

© LDA A Hand for Spelling 3b

Name . . . .

Trace over and then write the word.

cent   cent   cent   cent

Write each word carefully.

centre

central

century

Now practise your handwriting.

Put it in the centre.

Write the word cent in each box to make words.

Cover each word and write it from memory.

☐ re _____

☐ ral _____

☐ ury _____

Cent in a word often means something to do with a hundred. Join the words to the right meanings.

100 years   _____ enary

100 legs – or so it
was thought   _____ imetre

100th of a metre   _____ ury

100th of a dollar   _____ ipede

100 year anniversary _____

Name . . . .

Trace over and then write the letter pattern.

circ   circ   circ   circ

Write each word carefully.

circle   circular   circus

Now practise your handwriting.

The circus ring is circular.

Write the letter pattern circ in each box to make words.

Cover each word and write it from memory.

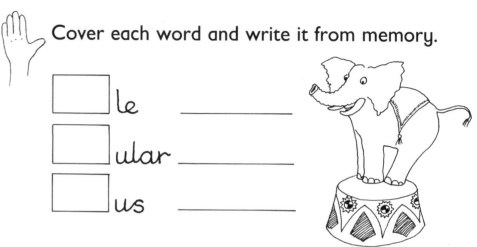

☐ le _____

☐ ular _____

☐ us _____

Now use some of these words to tell your friends about your visit to the circus.
Remember to use capital letters and full stops.

At the _____

_____

_____

_____

_____

_____

Name . . . .

Trace over and then write the word.

dent   dent   dent   dent

Write each word carefully.

dentist

dental

accident

Now practise your handwriting.

The dentist had an accident.

Write the word dent in each box to make words.

Cover each word and write it from memory.

[ ]ist _____

[ ]al _____

acci[ ] _____

Now use some of these words to explain what happened and finish the story.

Our car was in an _____
on the way to the _____. The
lights were smashed and the
bumper was broken. When we
got to the car park I _____

_____

_____

Name . . . .

Trace over and then write the word.

each   each   each   each

Write each word carefully.

beach   reach

teach   teacher

Now practise your handwriting.

The boat reached the beach.

Write the word *each* in each box to make words.

Cover each word and write it from memory.

b [ ] _____

r [ ] _____

t [ ] _____

t [ ] er _____

To the beach

Now use some of the words to label the pictures.

[ ]

[ ]

[ ]

Name . . . .

Trace over and then write the word.

east   east   east   east

Write each word carefully.

beast   least

feast   eastern

Now practise your handwriting.

He's a beast from the east.

Write the word *east* in each box to make words.

Cover each word and write it from memory.

b ☐ _____

l ☐ _____

f ☐ _____

☐ ern _____

Finish the rhyme.

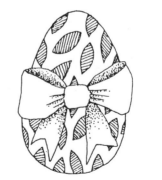

_____er eggs
Are a _____,
I have eaten
Ten, at _____ !

Name . . . .

Trace over and then write the letter pattern.

eigh   *eigh*   *eigh*   *eigh*

Write each word carefully.

eight

weigh

weight

neighbour

height

Now practise your handwriting.

Check my height and weight.

Write the letter pattern *eigh* in each box to make words.

Cover each word and write it from memory.

☐	t	_____
w ☐		_____
w ☐	t	_____
n ☐	bour	_____
h ☐	t	_____

Use *eigh* words to fill in the chart.

Age: _____ years

_____ : one metre _____een

cms

_____ : twenty _____

kilograms

60

Name . . . .

Trace over and then write the word.

even   *even*   *even*   *even*

Write each word carefully.

evening

seven

eleven

Now practise your handwriting.

The evening concert is at seven.

Write the word *even* in each box to make words.

Cover each word and write it from memory.

☐ ing _____

s ☐ _____

el ☐ _____

Now use some of these words to tell the story.
Remember to use capital letters and full stops.

_____

_____

_____

_____

Name . . . .

Trace over and then write the word.

ever   *ever*   *ever*   *ever*

Write the word *ever* in each box to make words.

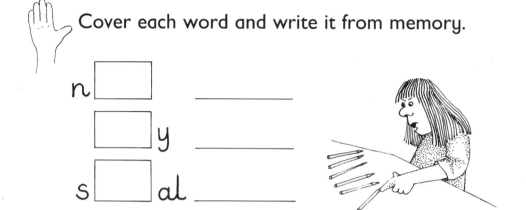

Cover each word and write it from memory.

n ☐ _____

☐ y _____

s ☐ al _____

Write each word carefully.

never

every

several

Now practise your handwriting.

Never, ever do that again.

Now find the small words in the following words.

never	every	however

62

Name . . . .

Trace over and then write the word.

fact   *fact*   *fact*   *fact*

Write each word carefully.

factory

satisfactory

manufacture

Now practise your handwriting.

The factory manufactures bolts.

Write the word *fact* in each box to make words.

Cover each word and write it from memory.

[ ] ory _____

satis [ ] ory _____

manu [ ] ure _____

Now find the small words in the following words.

factory	satisfaction	manufacture

Name . . . .

Trace over and then write the word.

hose   hose   hose   hose

Write each word carefully.

those

chose

whose

Now practise your handwriting.

Those firemen use hoses.

Write the word **hose** in each box to make words.

Cover each word and write it from memory.

t [ ] _____

c [ ] _____

w [ ] _____

Now crack the code to find the words.

a b c d e f g h i j k l m n o p q r s t u v w x y z
1 2 3 4 5 6 7 8 9 10 11 12 13 14 15 16 17 18 19 20 21 22 23 24 25 26

| 3 | 8 | 15 | 19 | 5 | _____

| 23 | 8 | 15 | 19 | 5 | _____

| 20 | 8 | 15 | 19 | 5 | _____

| 8 | 15 | 19 | 5 | _____

Name . . . .

Trace over and then write the letter pattern.

ible   *ible*   *ible*   *ible*

Write the letter pattern *ible* in each box to make words.

Cover each word and write it from memory.

B [ ] _____

poss [ ] _____

imposs [ ] _____

terr [ ] _____

Write each word carefully.

Bible

possible

impossible

terrible

Now practise your handwriting.

He reads from the Bible.

Now use some of these words to finish the sentences.

1. It was not _____ to climb the hill.

2. It would be _____ to swim across the ocean.

3. In the _____ wind, the fence blew over.

Name . . . .

Trace over and then write the letter pattern.

ight   *ight*   *ight*   *ight*

Write the letter pattern **ight** in each box to make words.

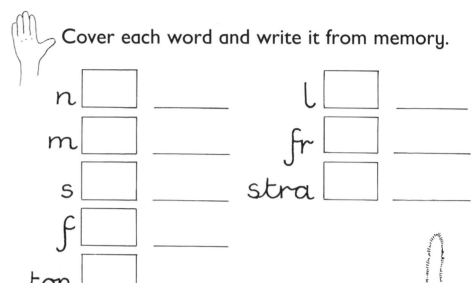 Cover each word and write it from memory.

n ☐ _____   l ☐ _____

m ☐ _____   fr ☐ _____

s ☐ _____   stra ☐ _____

f ☐ _____

ton ☐ _____

Write each word carefully.

night   might

sight

fight

tonight

light

fright

straight

Now practise your handwriting.

Cats might fight in the night.

Now use **ight** words to finish the poem.

At dead of _____ ,

By pale moon _____ ,

Two tom cats

In a _____ .

66

© **LDA** A Hand for Spelling 3b

Name . . . .

Trace over and then write the letter pattern.

ince   *ince*   *ince*   *ince*

Write each word carefully.

since

prince

princess

sincerely

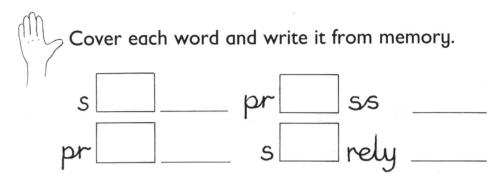

Now practise your handwriting.

The prince loved her sincerely.

Write the letter pattern *ince* in each box to make words.

Cover each word and write it from memory.

s ☐ _____   pr ☐ ss _____

pr ☐ _____   s ☐ rely _____

Now use these words to finish the Prince's letter to Cinderella.

The Palace
25th Sept. 1995

Dear Cinderella,
Ever _____ I saw you at
the ball . . . . .

Name . . . .

Trace over and then write the word.

king   king   king   king

Write each word carefully.

making

taking

baking

stocking

asking

Now practise your handwriting.

The King likes baking.

Write the word **king** in each box to make words.

Cover each word and write it from memory.

ma ☐ _____

ta ☐ _____

ba ☐ _____

stoc ☐ _____

as ☐ _____

Write these words in alphabetical order.

Now finish the pattern.

make		
	takes	
		baking
	shakes	
wake		

Name . . . .

Trace over and then write the word.

lies   lies   lies   lies

Write the word lies in each box to make words.

Cover each word and write it from memory.

f [ ] _____

rep [ ] _____

fami [ ] _____

jel [ ] _____

Write each word carefully.

flies   replies

families   jellies

Now practise your handwriting.

The flies flew round the jellies.

Write each word next to the right meaning.

[ ] a dessert

[ ] people related
     to each other

[ ] not the truth

[ ] answers

[ ] moves through
     the air

Name . . . .

Trace over and then write the letter pattern.

ment ment ment ment

Write each word carefully.

moment

cement

government

Now practise your handwriting.

The cement set in a moment.

Write the letter pattern **ment** in each box to make words.

Cover each word and write it from memory.

mo ☐ _____

ce ☐ _____

govern ☐ _____

Now read through this story and correct the spelling mistakes. Then finish the story.

The puppy jumped over the side of his bocks and ran into the garden where Dad was makeing a path. The sement hadn't set and in a moment he stept in it and left a trial of paw prints. Dad _____
_____

70

Name . . . .

Trace over and then write the letter pattern.

oose   oose   oose   oose

Write each word carefully.

goose

loose

choose

Now practise your handwriting.

There's a goose loose.

Write the letter pattern oose in each box to make words

 Cover each word and write it from memory.

g ☐ _____

l ☐ _____

ch ☐ _____

How many oose words can you find in the word search?

s	h	g	l	a	d	e
a	l	o	o	s	e	d
o	o	e	l	d	o	e
c	h	o	o	s	e	m
d	e	g	o	o	s	e
m	o	o	s	e	d	f

The opposite of tight is _____.

Name . . . .

Trace over and then write the letter pattern.

orry   orry   orry   orry

Write the letter pattern   orry   in each box to make words.

Cover each word and write it from memory.

s ☐ _____

l ☐ _____

w ☐ _____

Write each word carefully.

sorry

lorry

worry

Now practise your handwriting.

He was sorry to cause so much worry.

Now use these words to finish the poem.

I'm so _____

I've bumped your,_____

I was in a dreadful hurry.

Your _____'s dented —

Do not _____.

You can have

My shopping trolley!

Name . . . .

Trace over and then write the letter pattern.

ough   ough   ough   ough

Write each word carefully.

cough

rough

enough

though

plough

through

Now practise your handwriting.

He has a rough cough.

Write the letter pattern **ough** in each box to make words.

Cover each word and write it from memory.

c ☐ _____

r ☐ _____

en ☐ _____

th ☐ _____

pl ☐ _____

thr ☐ _____

Now write a sentence which includes each pair of words.

1. cough sweet _____

_____

2. plough horses _____

_____

3. through fence _____

_____

Name . . . .

Trace over and then write the letter pattern.

ould   *ould*   *ould*   *ould*

Write each word carefully.

couldn't

wouldn't

shouldn't

shoulder

boulder

mould

Now practise your handwriting.

Her shoulder moved the
boulder.

Write the letter pattern *ould* in each box to make
words.

Cover each word and write it from memory.

c ☐ n't _____   sh ☐ er _____

w ☐ n't _____   b ☐ er _____

sh ☐ n't _____   m ☐ _____

Rearrange the jumbled sentences.

1. shouldn't without You looking
cross first. _____

_____

2. by couldn't it myself. I do

_____

3. cheese you like with Do mould?

_____

Name . . . .

Trace over and then write the letter pattern.

ound   ound   ound   ound

Write each word carefully.

sound

mound

bound

found

wound

Now practise your handwriting.

I wound and bound the wound.

Write the letter pattern *ound* in each box to make words.

✋ Cover each word and write it from memory.

s [ ] _____

m [ ] _____

b [ ] _____

f [ ] _____

w [ ] _____

Write these words in alphabetical order.

Now finish the story using some of these words.
Remember to use capital letters and full stops.

The castle stood on a large
_____. As I looked out I heard
a strange _____. I waited and
then _____

_____

Name . . . .

Trace over and then write the letter pattern.

ount   *ount*   *ount*   *ount*

Write each word carefully.

count   *mount*   *mountain*

amount   *county*   *country*

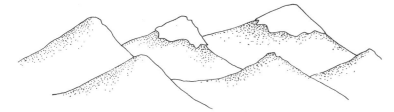

Now practise your handwriting.

Count the mountains.

Write the letter pattern **ount** in each box to make words.

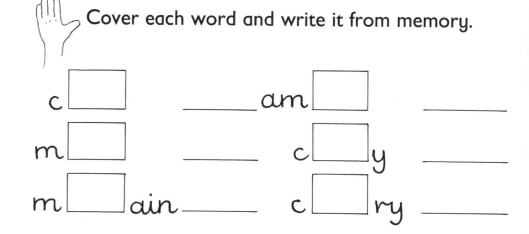

Cover each word and write it from memory.

c ☐ _____   ____ am ☐ _____

m ☐ _____   c ☐ y _____

m ☐ ain _____   c ☐ ry _____

Use some of these words to label the map.

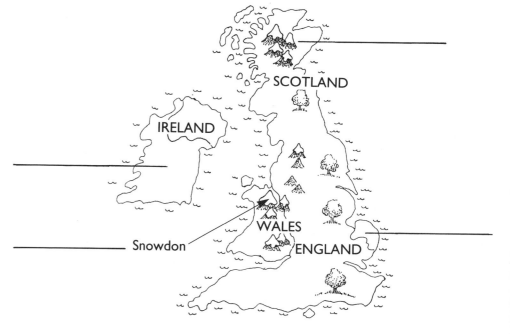

SCOTLAND

IRELAND

WALES

Snowdon

ENGLAND

Name . . . .

Trace over and then write the word.

port   port   port   port

Write each word carefully.

sport   report

airport   important

Now practise your handwriting.

She read an important report.

Write the word **port** in each box to make words.

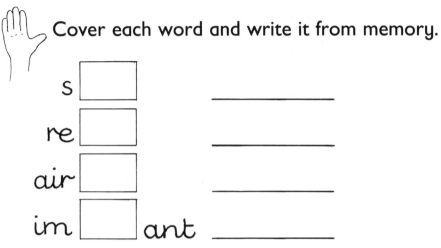 Cover each word and write it from memory.

s [ ]   _____

re [ ]   _____

air [ ]   _____

im [ ] ant   _____

Now write these words on the alphabet snake.

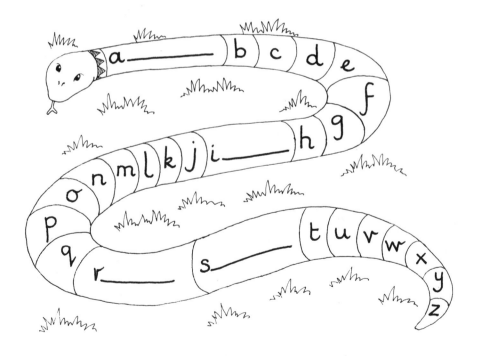

Name . . . .

Trace over and then write the word.

read   *read*   *read*   *read*

Write each word carefully.

ready   already

bread   thread

spread

Now practise your handwriting.

The bread is already spread.

Write the word **read** in each box to make words.

Cover each word and write it from memory.

	☐ y	_____
al	☐ y	_____
b	☐	_____
th	☐	_____
sp	☐	_____

Write these words in alphabetical order.

Now use some of these words to make a sandwich.

1. Take a loaf of _____ .

2. _____

3. _____

4. _____

© LDA A Hand for Spelling 3b

Name . . . .

Trace over and then write the word.

ream   ream   ream   ream

Write each word carefully.

dream   stream

cream   ice-cream

Now practise your handwriting.

I dream of ice-cream.

Write the word ream in each box to make words.

Cover each word and write it from memory.

d [   ] _____

st [   ] _____

c [   ] _____

ice-c [   ] _____

Use these words to finish the poem.

In my _____s
Are huge ____ - _____s,
And lemonade
Flows in _____s.
The trees are full
Of cherry pies,
While peppermint _____s
Fill the skies.

Name . . . .

Trace over and then write the word.

ring   ring   ring   ring

Write each word carefully.

string   spring

bring   bringing

during

Now practise your handwriting.

The spring brings us water.

Write the word ring in each box to make words.

Cover each word and write it from memory.

st ☐ _____

sp ☐ _____

b ☐ _____

b ☐ ing _____

du ☐ _____

Now print some of these words to fill the boxes.

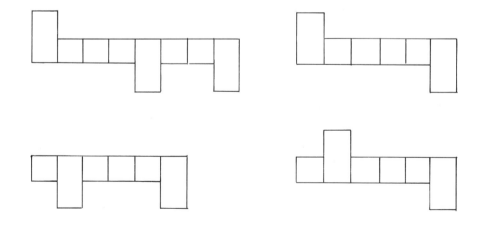

Name . . . .

Trace over and then write the letter pattern.

rown   rown   rown   rown

Write the letter pattern rown in each box to make words.

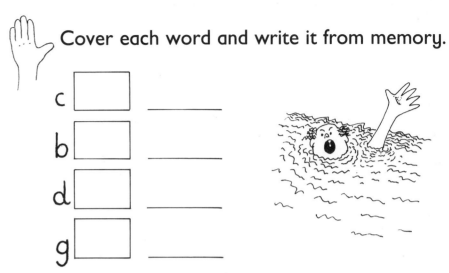

Cover each word and write it from memory.

c ☐ _____

b ☐ _____

d ☐ _____

g ☐ _____

Now write these words on the alphabet trail.

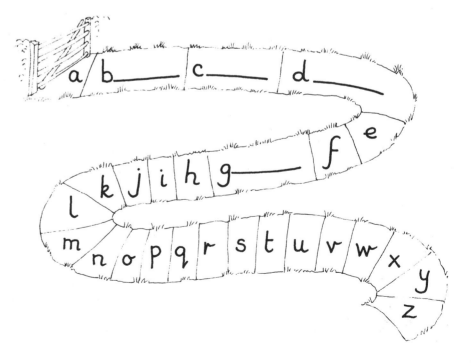

Write each word carefully.

crown   brown

drown   grown

Now practise your handwriting.

He's outgrown his crown.

Name . . . .

Trace over and then write the word.

rush   rush   rush   rush

Write each word carefully.

crush

brush

thrush

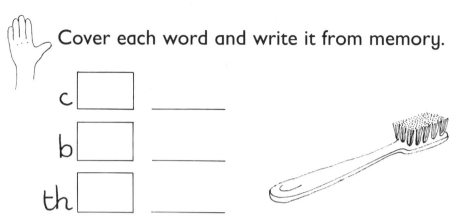

Now practise your handwriting.

The thrush family were
crushed.

Write the word rush in each box to make words.

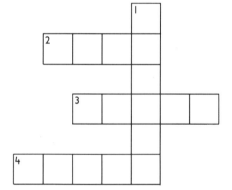

Cover each word and write it from memory.

c ▢ _____

b ▢ _____

th ▢ _____

Now use rush words to finish the crossword.

Across

2. Hurry.
3. You sweep with this.
4. Squash.

Down

1. A garden bird.

82

Name . . . .

Trace over and then write the word.

sand   sand   sand   sand

Write each word carefully.

sandy

sandals

thousand

Now practise your handwriting.

The sandals are on the sand.

Write the word **sand** in each box to make words.

Cover each word and write it from memory.

☐ y _____

☐ als _____

thou ☐ _____

Which **sand** words does this funny saying spell?

Two huge orange umbrellas sat
and nattered dreamily.

Can you think of funny sayings for sandy and sandals?

_____

_____

_____

Name . . . .

Trace over and then write the word.

self　　self　　self　　self

Write each word carefully.

herself　　　　himself

myself　　　　itself

yourself

Now practise your handwriting.

I do it by myself.

Write the word *self* in each box to make words.

Cover each word and write it from memory.

her [ ] _____

him [ ] _____

my [ ] _____

it [ ] _____

your [ ] _____

Now finish the pattern.

her	
	himself
it	
	myself
your	

84

© LDA A Hand for Spelling 3b

Name . . . .

Trace over and then write the word.

sent   sent   sent   sent

Write the word **sent** in each box to make words.

Cover each word and write it from memory.

	ence	_____
pre		_____
ab		_____

Write each word carefully.

sentence

present

absent

Now practise your handwriting.

The presents were sent by post.

Which **sent** words does this funny saying spell?

Six elderly neighbours talking endless nonsense came early.

Can you think of funny sayings for present and absent?

_____

_____

_____

_____

Name . . . .

Trace over and then write the letter pattern.

stor   stor   stor   stor

Write each word carefully.

store

story

stories

storm

stork

Now practise your handwriting.

The stork sheltered from the
storm.

Write the letter pattern *stor* in each box to make words.

Cover each word and write it from memory.

☐ e _____

☐ y _____

☐ ies _____

☐ m _____

☐ k _____

Now find all the *stor* words.

stormstoriesstorestorkstory

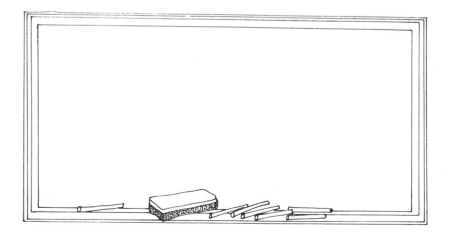

Name . . . .

Trace over and then write the letter pattern.

ture   ture   ture   ture

Write the letter pattern ture in each box to make words.

Cover each word and write it from memory.

cap [ ] _____

pic [ ] _____

punc [ ] _____

manufac [ ] _____

Write each word carefully.

capture

picture

puncture

manufacture

Now practise your handwriting.

He captured the picture.

Write each word and link it with a picture.

p _____

p _____

m _____

c _____

Name . . . .

Trace over and then write the word.

aught   aught   aught   aught

Write each word carefully.

caught

taught

naughty

daughter

laughter

Now practise your handwriting.

He taught the naughty pupils.

Write the word aught in each box to make words.

Cover each word and write it from memory.

c [   ] _____

t [   ] _____

n [   ] y _____

d [   ] er _____

l [   ] er _____

Write these words in alphabetical order.

Now use some of these words to finish the rhyme.

Covering chairs with glue
Was a _____ thing to do.
The teacher who _____ us
certainly _____ us
A lesson. So my friend
And I had a sticky end!

Name . . . .

Trace over and then write the word.

other   other   other   other

Write each word carefully.

mother

brother

another

bother

Now practise your handwriting.

Mother and brother hug each other.

Write the word *other* in each box to make words.

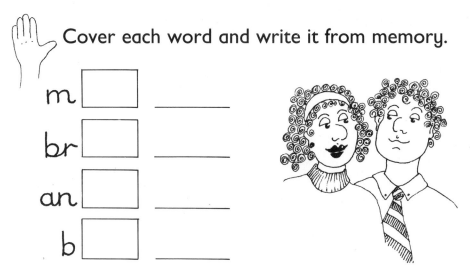

Cover each word and write it from memory.

m ☐ _____

br ☐ _____

an ☐ _____

b ☐ _____

Now find the small words in the following words.

mother	brother	another

Name . . . .

Trace over and then write the word.

ought   ought   ought   ought

Write each word carefully.

nought
bought
fought
thought
brought
drought

Now practise your handwriting.

The sun brought a drought.

Write the word ought in each box to make words.

Cover each word and write it from memory.

n ☐ _____   th ☐ _____

b ☐ _____   br ☐ _____

f ☐ _____   dr ☐ _____

Now finish the pattern.

buy	
	fought
think	
bring	

I _____ I'd _____ a chicken
But guess what I had done?
I'd left it at the checkout
And hadn't _____ it home.